YOU'RE THE VOICE
Nina Simone

© International Music Publications Ltd
First published by International Music Publications Ltd in 2002
International Music Publications Ltd is a Faber Music company
Bloomsbury House 74–77 Great Russell Street London WC1B 3DA

Series Editor: Anna Joyce
Editorial, production and recording: Artemis Music Limited
Design: IMP Studio
Photography supplied by Redferns Music Picture Library
Printed in England by Caligraving Ltd
All rights reserved

ISBN10: 0-571-52664-0
EAN13: 978-0-571-52664-2

To buy Faber Music publications or to find out about the full range of titles available,
please contact your local music retailer or Faber Music sales enquiries:

Faber Music Ltd, Burnt Mill, Elizabeth Way, Harlow, CM20 2HX England
Tel: +44(0)1279 82 89 82   Fax: +44(0)1279 82 89 83
sales@fabermusic.com   fabermusic.com

Nina Simone
Born Eunice Waymon
1933

A jazz singer, a protest singer, a pianist, an arranger and a composer, Nina Simone is a great artist who defies easy classification. Admired for her highly emotional and expressive delivery, her voice has an unusually deep, rich timbre, evoking and stirring her listeners' emotions in a skilful and varied fashion. Born Eunice Waymon in Tryon, North Carolina, USA, in 1933, and raised as one of eight children in a poor family, this remarkable child prodigy played piano since the age of four. With the help of her music teacher, who set up the 'Eunice Waymon Fund', she continued her general and musical education, ultimately attending the prestigious Julliard School of Music in New York. To support herself financially while she studied, she worked as an accompanist and gave piano lessons. Auditioning for a job as a pianist in an Atlantic City nightclub, she was told she had the spot if she would sing as well as play. Almost by accident, she began to carve a career as a singer of secular material, though her skills at the piano would serve her well throughout her career. In the late '50s she began recording for the small Bethlehem label. In 1959, her version of George Gershwin's I Loves You Porgy gave her a Top 20 hit - which would amazingly prove to be the only Top 40 entry of her career.

In the early '60s, she recorded no less than nine albums for the Candix label, half of them live. These unveiled her as a performer of nearly unsurpassed eclecticism, encompassing everything from Ellingtonian jazz and Israeli folk songs to spirituals and movie themes.

Simone's moody-yet-elegant vocals are unique, presenting a fiercely independent soul who harbours enormous (if somewhat hard-bitten) tenderness. Like many African-American entertainers of the mid '60s, Simone was deeply affected by the civil rights movement and burgeoning Black pride. Falling on turbulent times in the '70s, and following her divorce from husband/manager Andy Stroud, she encountered serious financial problems and became something of a nomad. However, she had unpredictable resurgence in 1987 when an early track, 'My Baby Just Cares For Me', became a big British hit after being used in a Chanel perfume television commercial.

Although Nina was called the 'High Priestess of Soul' and was respected by fans and critics as a mysterious, almost religious figure, she was often misunderstood. One of her best-known protest songs, Four Women, a bitter lament of four black women whose circumstances and outlook are related to subtle gradations in skin colour, was banned on Philadelphia and New York radio stations because 'it was insulting to black people...'

"Simone is an eclectic, who brings soulful qualities to whatever material she interprets." (Anon)

DON'T LET ME BE MISUNDERSTOOD

Backing

Words and Music by Bennie Benjamin, Gloria Caldwell and Sol Marcus

FEELING GOOD

Words and Music by Leslie Bricusse and Anthony Newley

Backing

I LOVES YOU PORGY

Words and Music by George Gershwin, Du Bose Heyward,
Dorothy Heyward and Ira Gershwin

I PUT A SPELL ON YOU

Words and Music by Jay Hawkins

Backing

LOVE ME OR LEAVE ME

Words by Gus Kahn
Music by Walter Donaldson

MOOD INDIGO

Words and Music by Duke Ellington,
Irving Mills and Barney Bigard

Backing

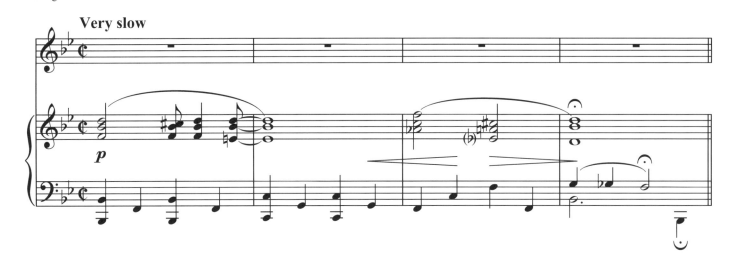

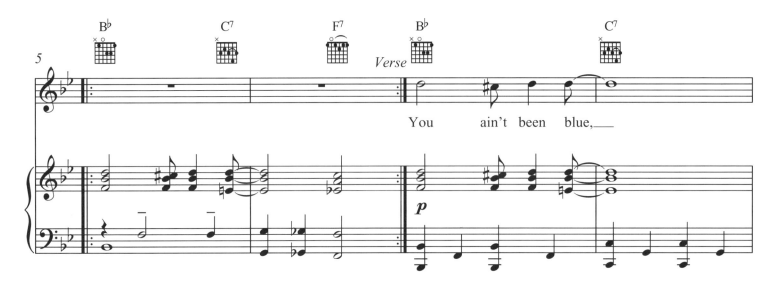

NE ME QUITTE PAS
(IF YOU GO AWAY)

Words by Rod McKuen
Music by Jacques Brel

MY BABY JUST CARES FOR ME

Words by Gus Kahn
Music by Walter Donaldson

Backing

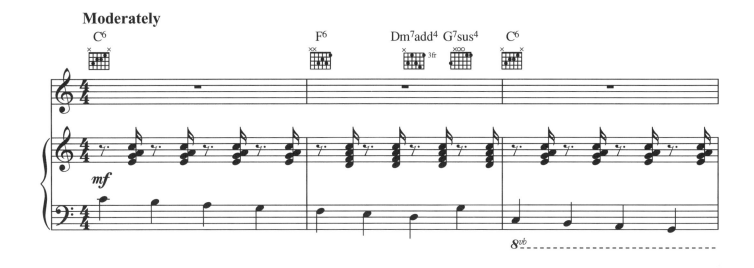

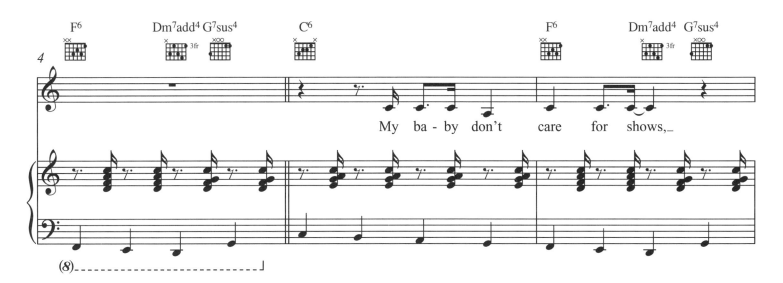

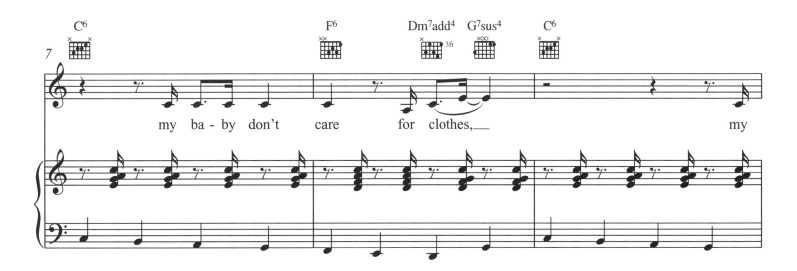

NOBODY KNOWS YOU
WHEN YOU'RE DOWN AND OUT

Words and Music by Jimmy Cox

Backing

TAKE ME TO THE WATER

Backing

Traditional
Arranged by Nina Simone

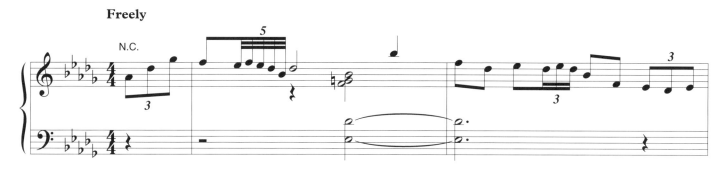

Take me to the wat - - - er, take me to the
right - - eous, none but the

YOU'RE THE VOICE

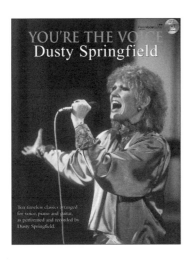

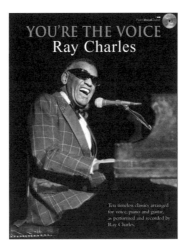

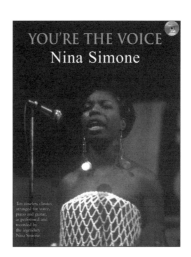

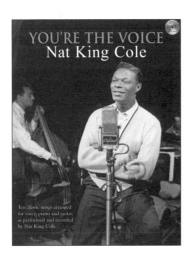

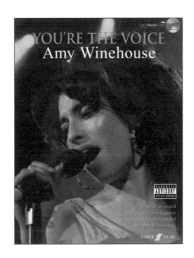

The outstanding vocal series from Faber Music
CD contains full backings for each song,
professionally arranged to recreate the sounds of the original recording

Shirley Bassey · James Blunt · Michael Bublé · Maria Callas · Eva Cassidy · Ray Charles
Nat King Cole · Sammy Davis Jr · Celine Dion · Aretha Franklin · Billie Holiday
Katherine Jenkins · Norah Jones · Tom Jones · Alicia Keys · Carole King · Madonna
George Michael · Dean Martin · Bette Midler · Matt Monro · Nina Simone
Frank Sinatra · Dusty Springfield · Barbra Streisand · Amy Winehouse

FABER _ff_ MUSIC

To buy Faber Music publications or to find out about the full range of titles available
please contact your local music retailer or Faber Music sales enquiries:

Faber Music Ltd, Burnt Mill, Elizabeth Way, Harlow CM20 2HX
Tel: +44 (0) 1279 82 89 82   Fax: +44 (0) 1279 82 89 83
sales@fabermusic.com   fabermusic.com   expressprintmusic.com